ACT COMPLETELY NORMAL!
DON'T LET ANYONE SUSPECT ANYTHING!
Whistle. Anything will do. Just look really relaxed.
O.K. Read this bit – quickly: We're going to tell
you something very important about this book.
The trouble is, it's such good news that if old
people and other adults hear it, they'll almost
certainly snatch the book out of your hands and
run away with it, shouting, "I've got one! I've
got one! Hooray!"

WAIT! IS THERE SOMEONE WATCHING YOU NOW?
Slowly – slowly – turn around and check. If there
is someone watching you, read this next bit later.

The thing is, this book gives you ...

HOLD IT!
No, false alarm. Sorry. But you can't be too
careful. Read this next bit very quickly indeed.

This book gives you complete freedom from
homework in lots of different ways. That's it.
That's it – now, quick, run like the wind! The
book must survive! The secrets must survive!

TOP
SECRET

Designed and illustrated by Chris, Joy and Zoe Mutter.
Additional illustrations by Mike Mosedale.

Published by Hodder Children's Books 1995.

10 9 8 7 6 5 4 3 2 1

Printed in Great Britain by Cox & Wyman Ltd, Reading, Berks

ISBN 0340620064

Hodder Children's Books
A division of Hodder Headline plc
338 Euston Road
London NW1 3BH

HOW TO DO YOUR HOMEWORK IN ✿TEN✿ SECONDS ✿ FLAT

by
Tim de Jongh
&
William Vandyck

Hodder
Children's
Books

a division of Hodder Headline plc

ABOUT THE AUTHORS

TIM DE JONGH has written things in a number of books. In 1992 he wrote an extra page for "Crime and Punishment" (by the Russian Fedor Doestoevsky). He stuck this into his copy and also the copy at the library. He has also written things and stuck them in his copies of "Moby Dick" (1993) and "The Witches Of Eastwick" (1994), all of which he thinks are a great improvement. Tim lives in Norwich together with many other people who also live there.

Thanks go to: Archbishops, horns, Tony Gubba, the A45, a dream, Ronnie Homerton M.A., Brian Gunn, Mark Bowen, clouds, Carl Bradshaw, Newsome, Polston, Adams, Crook, Milligan, Eadie, Robins, Sheron. Sub: Goss.

Thanks also go to Anne Clark, Vic Parker and everyone in the great land of Hodder and Stoughton.

WILLIAM VANDYCK is still a practising barrister. Since we last spoke, he has written and performed for the Children's Company, appeared in The Punt and Dennis Show on BBC1, travelled around Patagonia (it's brilliant by the way – do go), represented A Leading Motor Manufacturer in the Court of Appeal in a case about Stubbed Toes, Cut Fingers and Symptoms No Worse than a Common Cold, and failed to sell his flat. He likes to count amongst his friends, but they tell him to stop trying to show off, and then they go home.
What's new with you?

He would like to dedicate this book to his fab god-daughter Sophie Vandyck, his brilliant god-son to be Jack Firth, and his tremendous nephew, Joe Gardner. Don't argue over it now, you three.

Big Yo-s to: Kate and Charlie; Eddy and Louise; the still still brilliant parents; George and Ines Turner; Hutchinsons Worldwide Inc; Martin-Smiths; Sian, Eilian, Hywell, Rhian, Dylan and the Llews; Team One Paper Buildings; Mr Clive Priddle; Ms B.B.B. Berki; Uncle Ted (and not the waste of space in his downstairs room); Tim and Kate; Mike and Paula; Lissa; Tom Sanderson (why not?); Dave Tyler; Zurich; the continuing legal powerhouse that is AEW (you know who you are); Liz Tribe; Lucy Ogden NVQ; and Anne Clark and the mysterious "Vic" for being good. And Kathy.

4

CONTENTS

PREVENTING YOUR TEACHERS FROM SETTING HOMEWORK

Being able to do your homework in ten seconds flat is good, but it's even better to be able to prevent your teacher from setting you homework in the first place. This is by far the best policy (unlike "honesty" and the EC policy on fish in trousers which is so stupid they haven't even mentioned it yet). Anyway, in an ideal world your teacher would never set homework ever.

A recent survey showed that the best way of getting your teacher to never set homework was to lock them in the stationery cupboard, and then put a life-size cardboard cut-out of them at the front of the class. Stick on a speech bubble coming out of the mouth, saying, 'I'm not setting any homework. P.S. I'm not a cardboard cut-out.'

However this has a number of drawbacks:

A Your teacher may escape.

B You have to keep carrying the cardboard cut-out to Assembly and staff meetings so as not to arouse suspicion.

C If they do escape, they may not see the funny side, and set you double English homework forever.

So instead, this section gives you some finely tuned, carefully honed diversionary tactics to give you an excellent chance of not being set any homework.

From the Top

This note should distract your teacher sufficiently so they forget to set you any homework. Simply cut it out and give it to your teacher at the right time.

Governors' Meeting

Dear teacher,

There is to be a Governors' meeting in the school later today which will take place in your classroom.

Please clear all desks to the side and make sure everywhere is clean and tidy. Please also let the children leave five minutes before the end of school as the Governors may be here early and do not like to ever be seen. I myself have only seen one once.

Thank you for your co-operation. I am well. I hope you are.

Headteacher

Official Warning

Stick this poster up on your classroom door.

WARNING - HOMEWORKITUS!

There has been an outbreak of this highly contagious disease.

No homework should be set within a 40 mile radius until further notice.

KEEP ALL HOMEWORK BOOKS LOCKED UP.

This is true and not just made up. Be on your guard. Homework set in this area could have a nasty effect. Recent outbreaks of this illness have resulted in many teachers losing their jobs. So it's best not to set homework tonight, eh?

Signed

(signatures)

Everyone important

Scoop

Get out this newspaper cutting and read it during a lesson. When your teacher notices you're not paying attention – apologise and reluctantly show them what it says.

ASTRONOMICAL SHOW!

Tonight, tens of thousands of shooting stars will burn up as they enter the Earth's atmosphere.

A senior spokesperson from the British Astronomical Society said, 'It's going to be brilliant! Utterly brilliant! I can't wait. I've got sandwiches packed and everything. If teachers don't give homework tonight, children will have time to watch this amazing sight. They'll learn more about everything, instantly. It will all suddenly make sense - if only they aren't given any homework.'

A scientist who isn't a professor but wishes he was, said 'Yes, what an opportunity for children. I'm off to mix up some coloured liquids and do sums, then maybe they'll let me be a professor.'

The local authority has advised all teachers to cancel homework.

Advertisement

Slip this letter under the staff room door and it should put an instant stop to all homework.

FROM THE COUNTY COUNCIL

<u>NEW TEACHING VACANCY</u>

A new teaching vacancy has recently become available.

Middle School. Salary £150,000 (in cool unmarked cash). Class Teacher.

New post in a school in this area, for an easy going teacher who doesn't set homework. Children's references essential. Very short hours and children who are very quiet and get on with their work. Will have to look after the school anteater. But there is certainly none of that doing playground duty or having to shout, 'Who is making all that noise?'

A quite fantastic job. One only. If you think you could fill this post, please apply to the regional Education Officer, making absolutely sure you are eligible on the not setting homework bit.

CUT ALONG LINE

Honorary day off

Acting tip: *Say that you bumped into the Headteacher in the corridor, who asked you to give this note to your teacher.*

To:	**All teachers**
From:	**The Headteacher**
Re:	**Homework**

Tonight is the feast day of Saint Jibblings - the Patron Saint of No Homework.

I'm sure you are well aware of the story of Saint Jibblings, who in the 4th Century A.D. set up a shoe factory near the border of Mesopotamia. One day he heard a voice in the cupboard and (with zeal) went out and spent his life destroying homework. It was only years later that he discovered the voice he had heard had belonged to Sandra, his next door neighbour who had fallen asleep in there looking for some lunch.

Anyway, in honour of Saint Jibblings's special day, all pupils are to be let off tonight's homework.

Signed

Aurendown

The Headteacher

Fred Blythe

Somcone who was in the Headteacher's office

Meat Leadoch

Someone who was passing - and had always wanted to sign one of these

Professional letter

This letter works every time (as long as you don't use it on the same teacher more than once).

Nick Faldo

Expert, professional golfer
Available for all occasions -
weddings, fêtes, World Open Golf Championships etc

Dear teacher

I'm playing in a charity tournament at a course near here this evening (using floodlights if necessary) and I'd like this child to be my caddie.

Unfortunately this means they'll miss the chance of doing any homework, but this may well be the only time in their lives they'll have a chance to do this.

Think about it. Don't blow their dreams.

Best wishes,

Nick Faldo

Nick Faldo

P.S. Why is nobody else called Faldo?
P.P.S. Did you know that I'm brilliant at golf?
P.P.P.S. I can hit really wack that small golf ball.
WACK!

Promotions

Cut out these handy 'No homework' stickers and
stick them where your teacher will
see them.

No Homework
Tonight In Support
Of More Pay
For Teachers!

No Homework Tonight
In Support Of
The School Not Being
Closed Down!

No Homework Tonight In Support Of Teachers' Rights!

Teacher's award

Just fill in your teacher's name in the gap on this certificate, then cut it out and give it to them.

Certificate

The National Union of Teachers presents this gold award in recognition of

....

being an exemplary teacher who understands the needs and learning difficulties of children and does not set homework which might be a real downer for them, and make them far less receptive to work done in the classroom.

This certificate entitles the holder to a 10% rise in salary and better biscuits in the staff room at break.

Signed

The Head of the National Union of Teachers

CUT ALONG LINE

Blackmail

This is a special tactic to be used against Student Teachers. Cut out this letter and get the whole class to sign it.

Dear Student Teacher,

If you set us homework, you have to put all the books in the back of your car, or struggle with them on the bus, and then spend hours in the evening going through it all.

If you don't set homework, we won't squeal, and we'll be incredibly well-behaved when your supervisor comes in to watch a lesson.

Think about it. It makes sense. It's your degree. It's your career.

Signed

The whole class.

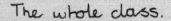

Dangerous Consequences

Cut out and leave this newspaper article where your teacher will see it.

THE NIGHT OF THE HOMEWORK MONSTER

Tonight is the night of the year that the Homework Monster is said to roam wild in this neighbourhood. Every year, strange things have

happened to teachers who set homework on this day.

Last year, Mrs Mutlow (who ignored the tale of the Homework Monster) got home to find she had lost all the paint from her walls and her kitchen was three feet deep in cornflakes. she said, 'I should have taken the rumour of the Homework Monster seriously. I certainly won't be setting any homework tonight. You can bet your life on that!'

Another teacher (who asked not to be named) is still too traumatised to be able to tell us what happened to him last year. However, he did manage the following words before bolting himself into his house. 'This Homework Monster means business. I still quake with fear at the thought of it. Any teacher who sets homework tonight is a mad, mad, mad person.'

ROTTERS NEWS

Here are some DIVERSIONARY TACTICS

for Advanced Students

Advanced Diversionary Tactic 1
ALL PURPOSE

This is a cunning plan for anyone with a portable tape recorder.

1 Take your tape recorder into school.

2 Tape the school bell. Keep the tape recorder handy.

3 Play the recording of the bell five minutes before the end of school, so the teacher has no chance to set homework.

If your school has no bell or buzzer, you could try taping the fire alarm instead. Be careful with this alternative – you could get into tremendous trouble for doing this if caught.

Advanced Diversionary Tactic 2
SCIENCE

Distract your teacher's attention just as the homework issue is about to crop up by showing them a stone and saying that it is 'Moonrock'. Produce this certificate to prove you're right. Add that it was lent to you by your Uncle with his full permission, although you have to return it before he gets back from work.

Certificate

This is an absolutely genuine piece of Moon Rock was brought back by me, Buzz Aldrin, and given to this pupil's Uncle.

OK?

CUT ALONG LINE

Advanced Diversionary Tactic 3
MATHS

Put this memo on your Maths teacher's desk before class.

TOO MUCH MATHS IN EUROPE.

Maths answers mountain: urgent action required

For every pupil whose Maths homework is set aside, this school will receive £500 from the EC and EC cushions.

Pages in Maths books must be left fallow.

Inspectors will check.

In fact, THAT MAY BE THEM NOW !

CUT ALONG LINE

Hand in this newspaper cutting just before your history teacher starts trying to set homework, and ask whether there's any point in studying homework any more.

do you hav e ti thou ght .

and wou dis

look a this do is April up 29th idiot. That inco

'ALL HISTORY IS WRONG!' says Professor Bradshaw.

Professor Bradshaw of the University of Finsbury Park says he has discovered a time capsule buried in the time of James 1. Startlingly, it contains gravel, soil and an old Coke can.

'This proves all History is wrong,' said the Professor yesterday.

'And in no way is this just rubbish. **Okay, come and have a go…**'

TEN SECOND HOMEWORKS

Here are some homeworks which are so easy you can do them in ten seconds flat.

You may wonder why we're setting you homework when this book is supposed to be about getting you out of it.

Well, the point is that when you've done even a tiny bit of homework, you can **honestly** say you've done **some** homework in that subject. Indeed, if someone doesn't believe you, you can take a lie detector test as to whether you've done some homework or not - which you will pass, because you did do **some**. Indeed, you can go to your headteacher and say, 'My teacher doesn't believe I've done any homework but I have. I demand a jury trial to clear my good name, or at least £5 not to mention this again. Also, a day off school, some computer games, and top marks in all my end of year exams.'

P.S. See also 'How To Get Away With Absolutely Anything', a very fine piece of literature, a classic of its time – which only coincidentally happens to have been written by us. Here's what was said about it. 'It's a classic example of perfect prose meeting the imagination. They weren't paid enough.'

Geography 1

You can honestly say you've studied map reading when you've looked at this for a bit.

Rolf Harris =

 = Church with no Rolf Harris

Church with spoon =

= Church without spoon

Church with supermarket =

 = Church with 9 screen cinema, ten pin bowling alley

 = Almost certainly a church, I can't quite see from here.

None of the above =

 = The New York Fish Exchange

Tourist Information =

= Tourist Lies

Battle =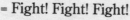

 = Fight! Fight! Fight!

= Rolf Harris Experimentation Centre

Dropped Wallet containing £5 =

Jimmy Hill's House =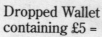

= Jimmy Hill's Friend's House

Jimmy Hill likes cheese =

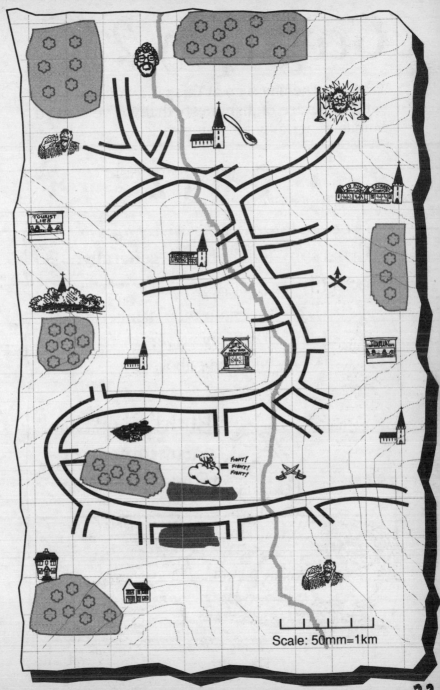

Scale: 50mm=1km

23

Geography 2

When you've had a go at this quiz, you can say without a trace of dishonesty that you've studied human geography for homework.

QUIZ

Put a circle around the correct answer.

Geography teachers are generally:

(a)   a bit dull
(b)   keen on mountaineering
(c)   not very clever
(d)   all of the above

Geography 3

More maps (it's a favourite topic).

Sailors used to navigate by the stars - a technique still used today by sailors in emergencies. To help them, they join the stars up with lines to make pictures (known as constellations), like the Plough.

Here are some star constellations quite forgotten by everyone. Some are more useful for navigation than others. Spot the more useful ones.

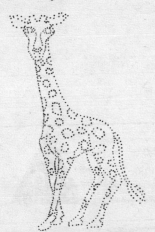

1 Bob the Giraffe   **2** Darren the Warrior

3 Jimmy Hill's Beard   **4** The M62

Maths 1

Maths homework can take forever.
Not this one, though.

See if you can successfully operate this flow chart to a conclusion.

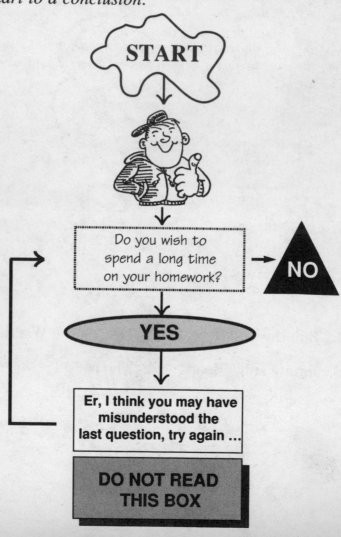

Maths 2

Try this ten second arithmetic homework.

1. Think of a number. It can be any number at all for this to work. That is, it can be odd or even, a positive or a negative number or a fraction, although you may find it easier the first time you do this homework to try a positive whole number.

-3 $2\,2\frac{1}{2}$

92 54·5

37 61

2. That's it.

History 1

Read the following, and you can honestly say that you have not only studied some of the writings about the very nature of history, but that you also did a multiple choice history questionnaire.

Ye olde historical questionnaire

Put a circle around the correct answers to the statement below.

If history teaches us anything, it teaches us:

A Anything.

B To opt for an alternative subject at the earliest opportunity.

C Dates are best eaten.

D Not to repeat the mistakes of the person from whom we are copying.

E 'Forgive and forget' is a sensible, generous, warm hearted approach to life. So history should be banned.

F If you really are forced to learn historical dates, a good way of memorising them is to write them on your arm just before going into the test.

History 2

History teachers usually set you huge amounts of homework, so here's another ten second one to help you out.

True or false?

Florence Nightingale batted left-handed for Warwickshire in 1975-76.

Answer
Oh, stop messing about, you know the answer. Do let's get on.

History 3

More history homework for you to take ten seconds in studying.

The Battle Of Trafalgar 1805

The English defeated the French in the sea battle of Trafalgar. Nelson sent a signal before the battle from his ship using flags. It said, 'England Expects Every Man To Do His Duty'. Here are some more flag signals he could have used.

1 How are you doing ?

2 Do Not Eat - battle in progress.

3 After-battle cocktails here for those with coupons.

4 How do you sail this thing?

5 To fire cannons: light blue touch paper and retire.

6 No overnight parking or camping.

7 We are sinking.

8 Is this the correct flag to signal the commence of battle?

History 4

Yet more history homework!

In 1666 there was a great fire in London, only a year after the height of a great plague. Here is one of the pages from a diary written at the time by Sir Samuel Pepys. This particular page is seldom read, but will provide you with everything you need to know.

Monday September 1st

Poor unfortunate Mrs. Simpson died of Plague yesterday. What a kind, caring, sweet woman she was. I must remember to put her outside the backdoor for the man to collect. A great fire burns in London. Can't think what to write about it much so here's a picture.

Table tennis game with the Bishop of London 12.40. Chris Wren coming round to see about kitchen extension 2.30. High tide 3.57. National Holiday in Wales.

Religious Studies

There's no need for Religious Studies homework to make you feel guilty. Answer this question and you'll be able to look your teacher straight in the eye when you're asked if you've done any.

There is a school of thought (albeit a small school, which has in fact been closed down) that says that there was an 11th Commandment which Moses didn't have room for on the two stone tablets he had with him.

Look at the extra commandments below. Which do you think is the most likely to have been the 11th Commandment?

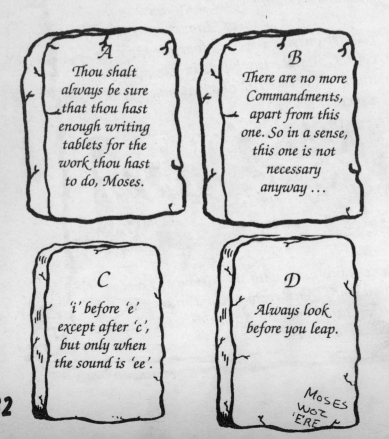

A
Thou shalt always be sure that thou hast enough writing tablets for the work thou hast to do, Moses.

B
There are no more Commandments, apart from this one. So in a sense, this one is not necessary anyway ...

C
'i' before 'e' except after 'c', but only when the sound is 'ee'.

D
Always look before you leap.

MOSES WOZ 'ERE

English

Most English homework involves a lot of reading. Just get someone who knows the book to tell you how the story goes. Use the ten second homework below if you are given any English Language work to do.

Which of the words in brackets should go in the gap in the following sentences? The first has been done for you as an example.

1 He chose the most <u>explosive</u> present.
(expensive, explosive)

2 When it comes to marking English work, English teachers make a point of being _____ .
(fair/quick)

3 A good English teacher is a _____ English teacher.
(clear, careful, helpful, supportive, inspiring, dead)

4 English teachers always admire _____ questions.
(relevant, intelligent, thoughtful, their own)

5 An English teacher will never let his or her own personal feelings interfere with the _____ .
(lesson, constant flow of bitter and sarcastic remarks)

Science

It's perfectly logical to say that you've done some Science homework when you've read the following.

When Neil Armstrong, the first man to stand on the moon, came down the ladder of the moon landing craft of Apollo 11, he said, 'That's one small step for a man, one giant leap for mankind.'

Here are some things he might have said instead.

It's all made of cheese!

So Huston, where exactly am I? No don't tell me...it begins with 'M' doesn't it?

Hello Rover, how did you get here?

Hang on - I need my towel and a book to read.

Great! It looks like there's a sale on.

HOMEWORK EXCUSES!

O.K. So you haven't done your homework, and it's time to hand it in. We all know the scenario.

Scene. A classroom. Day. The pupils are sitting, waiting for the teacher. Some of them have homework ready to hand in, others don't. A lion enters. It has ginormous teeth. It opens its mouth, like this:

Slowly, it advances on the people without homework...

OH NO, we appear to have the wrong scenario. This is the scenario with which we are all too familiar:

Scene. A classroom. Day. Pupils are sitting at their desks. A teacher enters, snarls and says, 'Okay, it's time to hand your homework in, and anyone who doesn't have it is in real trouble.'

Phew! So, it's crunch time. If you can't cover your exit with smoke bombs, here are some cast iron excuses to use.

Secret Filming Memo

Copy out this memo and leave it lying around just before you have to mention you haven't done your homework.

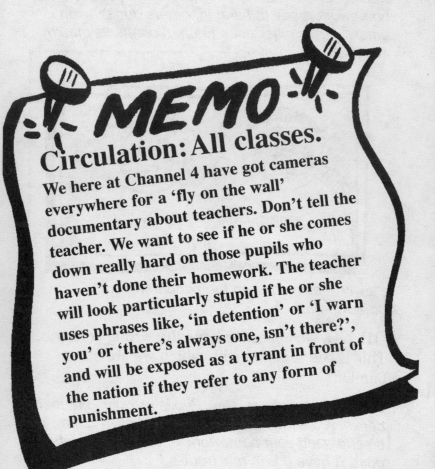

MEMO

Circulation: All classes.

We here at Channel 4 have got cameras everywhere for a 'fly on the wall' documentary about teachers. Don't tell the teacher. We want to see if he or she comes down really hard on those pupils who haven't done their homework. The teacher will look particularly stupid if he or she uses phrases like, 'in detention' or 'I warn you' or 'there's always one, isn't there?', and will be exposed as a tyrant in front of the nation if they refer to any form of punishment.

Form Filling

Ask your teacher to help you fill in this form by filling in their name and subject. Say that they needn't worry about the rest.

FOR THE ATTENTION OF THE TEACHER ASSESSMENT AND ADVISORY PANEL (TAAAP)

Teacher's name ....

Subject ....

Reaction to not handing in homework (circle one)

a) Wonderfully tolerant and understanding of problems facing children today.

b) Average reaction.

c) Behaved like Hitler. Extraordinary ranting and raving. Completely unreasonable. Will send the boys round.

Recommendation for pay rise next year (circle one)

a) Increase

b) Stay the same

c) Reduce

d) Give their pay to charity

CUT ALONG LINE

Homework Donation

Cut out this receipt and hand it in instead of your homework.

HOMEWORK RECEIPT

Your pupil is to be congratulated for nobly submitting their homework to the **'Help A European Child At School'** project.

.... pieces of homework received with thanks.

Signed

Chairperson of the 'Help A European Child At School' project

P.S. THIS IS EXTREMELY TRUE, AND MY DAD IS BIGGER THAN YOUR DAD **SO DON'T MAKE ANY TROUBLE.**

Pet Problems

Simply cut out, fill in and use this certificate.

Certificate

This is to certify that I, Mr. Dog, also known as:

....

did eat the homework of:

....

on: ....

Signed: ....(The dog)

Witnessed by:

....(Another dog)

PS GGGGGrrrrrrrrrrrrrrr!
PPS Any more choc drops left?
PPPS Here is a portrait of me as a young dog.

All-Purpose Letter

This completely teacher-proof letter is suitable for any occasion.

Memo To All Classes
Dear Teacher,

I happened to bump into this child on their way to school and to their surprise, demanded to see their homework. I'm sorry to say that I did it in a rather aggressive manner.

Anyway, that's not the point. No, the point is that the homework was just brilliant. Really excellent. So good, in fact, that I've sent it by chauffeur to all the other schools in the area.

Well done for having such a good pupil. I suppose this means you won't be seeing the homework for a bit.

I hope you are well. I am.

Signed

Headteacher

Cutting Out Homework

This one is best used the day after you've had a haircut.

Dear teacher,

I have an apology to make. I was cutting your pupil's hair, and I noticed that it has the particularly rare structure and root system known as 'Non-slap Five'. I have never come across this before in all my years of cutting hair. I asked your pupil if I could study it for a while, but they said it was out of the question as they had to do their homework.

I'm afraid I delayed your pupil by cutting one side of their hair in a rather silly way. They couldn't leave without making everybody think your school allowed pupils to have silly haircuts. Of course, I now realise that this was terribly wrong and I am filled with remorse for preventing your pupil from doing the homework you set.

I would like to make this up to you. If you buy three haircuts for yourself only, on any afternoon next week, I will only charge you for two and a half.

With love from your local barber

Prior Engagement

Cut this out, insert your name at the bottom, and give it to your teacher.

Acting tip: *look a little tired when handing this one in.*

MINUTES OF RESIDENTS' COMMITTEE MEETING
NO. 29871

Present: Mr. Freter (Member no. 391)
           Ms. Tarr (Member no. 455)
           Mr. Lowe (Member no. 497) - representing
           the Janion and Bunce families
           M   (Member no. 501)

1. The minutes of the last meeting were read and agreed.

2. Member no. 391, chairing the meeting, apologised for the way in which the meeting had effectively been sprung on everyone without any warning. He apologised particularly to Member no. 501, who really had only been told about it at the last minute.

3. Member no. 391 expressed his deep regret that it was his fault that Member no. 501 would have no time in which to do homework, but stated that this situation was completely unavoidable as Member no. 501 just had to be at the meeting.

4. Important things were discussed, for a long time.

5. Shaking his head sadly, Member no. 391 concluded the meeting by again apologising to Member no. 501 for forcing him into a no-homework situation.

Signed

John L. Freter
(Member no. 391)

Cc Member no. 501

Medal Ceremony

Insert your name on this certificate (in fancy writing if you can) along with a time, date, and venue to suit you. Hand it in to your teacher, saying you are sorry that the surprise ceremony clashed with the time that you had set aside for your homework.

Acting tip: *try and fake a glow of quiet pride.*

Brave and Observant Young Lifesaver of the year

This is to certify that ....
has been awarded the title of **Brave and Observant Young Lifesaver of the year (BOYL).**

The BOYL noticed that three young children were trapped on a blazing runaway train. The BOYL leapt aboard, and then ran along the top of the train (ducking for tree branches and tunnels), keeping the children calm by singing the theme tune from 'Casey Jones, the Railroad Driver'. The BOYL put out the fire by knocking away the supporting leg of a water tower which was next to the track. The BOYL then brought the train to a halt just in time to stop it crashing into the local hospital (up to which the rails had been laid in something of an administrative error).

The surprise Award Ceremony and Medal Presentation was held at:

on: *and took several hours.*

Signed

Gordon Catford	**Kim Franklin**	**Joe Gardner**
Lord Mayor	**Lady Mayor**	**Cleaner**

OFFICIAL SEAL

Productivity Drive

Get a friend to write your name in the middle of this letter, and sign it at the bottom.

Dear Teacher,

As you will recall from department circular memo FG@119837, we are at present testing the usefulness of homework. We will be monitoring the progress of selected pupils in your subject, to whether those that do homework perform any better than those who do not.

To this end, your pupil ....
has been selected as

☑ a no homework
pupil

☐ a homework
pupil

and we would be very grateful if you would therefore

☐ keep a copy of all
their homework
available for
inspection

☑ set this pupil no
homework all
term

Thank you for your co-operation. Please do not forget that the annual pay of teachers, including yourself, is dealt with by this department. It would be a shame if for some reason your pay were to go down.

Yours sincerely,

"No Homework Pupil — OFFICIAL!"

Colin Rossington-Nixon.
[Person in charge of
Homework Productivity Study]

Important
Letter not valid without official
rectangular stamp here

Education Cutbacks

Get the same friend as before to fill your name into this letter and also sign it.

Dear Teacher,

Hello again. We are all too aware of the need for saving costs in education. In the past there have been cutbacks on textbooks, equipment and pay.

Now, for an experimental period, we have decided to try cutting back on the amount of work that you, as a teacher have to do. In your case this means you are excused from marking the homework of your pupil

.... The pupil concerned has been advised to send their work elsewhere for marking (so you will never see it).

Thank you for your co-operation.

Yours sincerely,

Colin Rossington-Nixon.
[Person in charge of
Homework Savings Scheme, too]

<u>Important</u>
**Letter not valid
without
another official
rectangular
stamp here**

"No Homework
Pupil —

ANOTHER
OFFICIAL STAMP"

Health Certificate

This Health Certificate will get you off a whole week's homework. Just insert today's date, and it's ready for you to use.

HEALTH CERTIFICATE

This person has been officially diagnosed as suffering from Gammogiariseiasis. (This is actually a very rare disease, which is probably why you haven't heard of it.)

Anyway the point is that this person should not come in to contact with, or even *see*, really, anything to do with homework for the week of

....

....

Signed

R. Honester

R. Honester
FRCS, NO, REALLY
A Specialist In This
Kind Of Thing

S. COLES

S. Coles
FRCS, OK,
ITSA, FIB
A Specialist In
A Similar Kind
Of Thing

Insurance Claim Form

Tell your teacher that you were burgled, and that your homework was taken. They won't believe this to start with, as it is unlikely that a burglar would want to steal homework, but you can 'prove' your story by showing this copy of a page of your family's insurance claim form.

DEAD DODGY CLAIMS INC.

Draw a sketch showing the burglar's point of entry.

burglar → [door] ← window

Suspected Method Of Entry of Burglar:

We believe the burglar used abseiling equipment, oxy-acetylene cutters, a trained monkey, or the small spiky bit on Swiss Army Pen-knives.

Items lost:
Video, TV, Stereo and 15 CDs (including two copies of 'Take That And Party' - one was a spare)
French Horn, clarinet, trombone, maracas, stylophone
Ear plugs
Briefcase containing: wallet, mobile phone, calculator, Electronic Personal Organiser
One piece of homework
Gameboy
Sheet music for Stylophone

Animal Rescue

It would be a fairly hard-hearted teacher that would not forgive you for not doing your homework when you hand in this letter.

NSPCA

Dear Teacher,

Yesterday your pupil brought in a small, furry animal which had been abandoned. The little fellow looked so sweet with his tiny front paws resting on the edge of the shoebox your pupil was carrying him in, with his little eyes peeping out imploringly! It was as if he was saying, 'be my friend! I'll be good if you'll be nice to me.'

But - oh horror! I suddenly realised (because I have spent years caring for animals), that the poor little thing did not have long to live, even though he was very young, and should have had a long life of bouncing healthily and happily over big grassy open spaces, and smiling. There was nothing, it seemed, that I could do to help.

But then your pupil started to stroke the tiny creature, whispering comforting things in its ear. With food, drink and care - but most of all, with pure and simple love - the little thing began, slowly, to ascend the long and difficult path to recovery. It took hours and hours, but thanks to your pupil, the little chap is now perfectly all right, and will have that happy, healthy life after all.

Of course, this meant that there was absolutely no question of your pupil having any time to do homework. I'm sure you understand.

Yours sincerely,

Jonathan Gilbert Stokes

Jonathon Gilbert Stokes
(Animal Carer, First Class)

tear drop!

HOMEWORK EXCUSES FOR ADVANCED STUDENTS

So, you've used up all the excuses in the last chapter and you still haven't got to the end of the year. The time has come to set your sights higher. The following excuses are for advanced students only. They are for students who think big. They are excuses that have been used by students who have gone on in life to become Cabinet Ministers, Archbishops, Ambassadors, Admirals and Oil Rig Drilling Platform Supervisors. There are Bravery Points at the bottom of each page.

The more points you score, the more likely you are to become Prime Minister or to get a top job in a company.

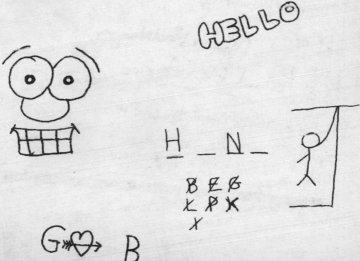

Artistic Sacrifice

Don't wait until the last second to hand your teacher this letter. Present it with pride the minute you get to school.

Dear Sir or Madam,

The most important piece of papier mâché sculpture this year is called, 'The Lion, The Witch and Philip Schofield.' We're sure that the sculpture will help to bring peace between nations.

We were racing towards finishing it until - tragedy! We ran out of paper! And we only had Philip Schofield's nose to do.

Fortunately your pupil walked past and gave us their homework, even though they knew this would get them into trouble.

Well, the sculpture's finished and it looks excellent. Please don't be too hard on this pupil. They have played a vital part in making progress towards World Peace.

Yours

Alison Hazlebum

Kaunt McFoot *Zoe Mutter*

Papier Mâché People Against War

PS
How do you spell 'Papier Mâché?

Paper Plane

Hand your teacher this letter and look hopeful.

CUT ALONG LINE

Dear teacher,

Your pupil is currently running first in the All Britain Paper Aeroplane Championship. They may win your school a computer if you don't give them grief about using their homework for it. (The paper was just the right kind for your pupil's excellent design.)

Signed

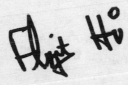

Chairperson of the All Britain
Paper Aeroplane Championship

BRAVERY
1
POINT

Dutiful Pupil

Acting tip: *hum a rousing tune as you hand your teacher this note.*

Dear Teacher,

Hello, it's the Headmaster again. This time I stopped your pupil for a different reason.

We needed some new lyrics for the school song, as the old ones were written in 1893, and had worn out. Write some more, I told your pupil, although I expect you won't be able to do your homework as well. Imagine my delight when they came up with this:

'Oh school! How brilliant it is!
How all-round good and not at all boring.
And isn't it great when there's an election
and we all get a day off
as the school is used as a polling station.'

I hope you'll agree that sacrificing homework to come up with this spirited new school song has been well worth it.

Love and kisses

Mmm Mmeo

Headteacher

CUT ALONG LINE

Useful Excuse –
Science Subjects

Try saying this:

I had an idea which might lead to a process of ensuring clean drinking water in poor countries. Faced with a choice of either doing my homework, or pressing on with an idea that could save thousands of lives every day, I chose the latter. Was I so wrong?

Then hand over this diagram.

If asked what the process actually is, you can say that your proposal is with the Patent Office, who have advised you not to give any further details at this time.

Useful Excuse – Arts Subjects

Say that after thinking about career advice you have been given from all the people you most respect, you feel that recently you have not devoted enough time to considering the job that you should do. So last night, you practised the Vocational Stage of Training For Real Life No.1. This was *Being An Announcer*.

Clear your throat and then say in a loud, posh voice:

We would like to announce the non-arrival of homework this morning. This was due to homework difficulties. We apologise for any inconvenience this may cause. Thank you.

Hitting the Right Note

Here is a note for you to pass around the class,
until your teacher catches you and demands to see
it. Only show it very reluctantly.

> What am I going to do? I
> haven't got any homework to
> hand in, because I've been
> spending my time caring
> for a sick and elderly
> relative. I'm sure our
> teacher won't believe me
> if I own up. Also, just
> recently, the relative has
> been getting so sick and
> elderly that if she hears
> I've got into trouble over
> homework because I've
> been caring for her - well, it
> could be the last straw!
> Especially as I've had to keep
> my relatives sickness secret
> from the rest of the family
> for reasons I can't go into
> now. So even if this story
> was checked with them they
> wouldn't know anything about
> it.

Will to Win

Insert your teacher's name in the blank spaces.

Buney Bunny and Buuny

To Whom It May Concern

We the partners of Buney, Bunny and Buuny do solemnly swear that the pupil who is the bearer of this document was delayed over the reading of a Last Will and Testament of a deceased relative, which was to the following effect:

That the said pupil is to allocate, within the foreseeable future, the fund of £500,000 (five hundred thousand pounds), tax free (with a souvenir tankard which will be engraved) to good, understanding, forgiving teachers.

We swear that, due to necessary attendance at the reading of the Will, the said pupil was unable to do the homework that had been set. We hope you'll understand.

Incidentally, think what you could do with £500,000,

.... A new home? A

world cruise for you and the rest of the

.... family?

You would never have to teach again!

Signed

Buney

Bunny

Buuny

Buney   Bunny   Buuny

CUT ALONG LINE

National Security

Acting tip: *look as serious as you can when you hand this in.*

Dear Teacher,

Your pupil has been of great assistance in the continual fight against ~~░░░░░░░░░░░~~

For reasons of National Security, we are unfortunately unable to tell you the time, date, duration, or nature of the assistance provided. However, it was significant. It also meant that your pupil was unable to do homework.

That this is true can be proved by the fact that ~~░░░░░░░░~~, and also that ~~░░░░░░░░░~~, or ~~░░░ some~~ ~~░░░░░░░░░░░░░ and thing░░░░░░ ░ fish~~ ~~░░░░░░~~ mayonnaise ~~░░░░░░░░░░~~ serve hot.

Yours very sincerely

MI5 Officer

PS Certain passages of this letter have had to be blacked out, because ~~░░░░░░░░░░░░░░░░░~~). Of course, we could tell you, but then we'd have to ~~░░░░░░░░~~ If you require further information, please write to (~~░░░░░░░░░░~~ ~~░░░░░~~

PPS Parts of the last passage have had to be ~~░░░░░░░░░░~~ ~~░░░░░~~

Last Resort Homework Excuse - Science

Try saying this to your Science teacher:

You know that you once said that Science needed imagination and innovation. Well, I decided to write my homework for last night in mirror writing. Unfortunately, that means that it is still on the mirror.

HOMEWORK TO HAND IN

Sometimes, just for a change, say, you might want to hand some homework in. For example, if your teacher has given you the option of handing homework in or being executed, and has already bought the guillotine and, say, been practising with melons, with an increasingly manic smile, shouting, 'Weeeeceee! Chop! Yesssss!'

If so, here are some homeworks on all imaginable subjects for you to hand in, which will get you full marks every time. All the homeworks are fully-guaranteed, ready-made, absolutely fresh, pre-processed, hand-crafted, machine-tooled, no batteries required and no strings attached. They also do not require any previous experience.

Maths

Say you did your maths homework as a poem.
Then hand in a book containing the poem
below:

Two.
What a number
Not straight unlike a cucumber
But curved, sleeping in a slumber
Between one and three,
You are used by ships in the Humber
To count lumber
Two.
You are my sort
of number.

Now I shall rumba.

English 1

Your teacher will at some stage probably ask you to prepare a presentation on a topic of your choosing. Here's how you can do a talk with no preparation, no matter how long your talk is supposed to last for.

When it's your turn, say that your talk is called 'The Power Of Silence, and How it Makes People Feel Uncomfortable'. Then say nothing.

After a while people will begin to fidget. Nod as if to say, 'I told you so' every time this happens. When your allocated time is up, say, 'Thank you very much' and sit down.

Art

An artist called René Magritte once put a pipe in a box with a note underneath which said, 'This is not a pipe.'

This is not a pipe

This kind of art is called 'Surrealism'. It uses the unexpected to challenge the way we look at the world.

If you're asked to do any Art homework, simply find some old homework (it doesn't matter what subject). Then mount it on a piece of card and write underneath, 'This is not some homework.'

THIS IS NOT HOMEWORK.

English 2

If your English teacher gives you a title and asks you to write a poem on that particular subject, here's how to do it in ten seconds and appear really clever.

A 'haiku' is a Japanese form of poem, (no - really, it is) which has to have only three lines, with a total of seventeen syllables.
For example

A summer breeze.
I see that in one way,
It is a little like life.

All you have to do is just adapt the title you've been given to four syllables, and substitute it for the first line. For example, if you were given 'Fire' as your title, you could write something like:

The fire burns bright.

Then add the last two lines:

The fire burns bright.
I see that in one way,
It is a little like life.

Remember to tell your teacher that you decided to write a haiku poem, otherwise they may think you have just been lazy.

IMPORTANT TIP
If you're given something in the plural as your title - like 'holidays' - remember to change 'it is' in the last line to 'they are'.

Science 1

Hand in the piece of paper below and say that you have written your homework in scientifically invisible ink, which shows up when the paper is heated. Then hold a match under the page until it catches fire. If your school has working smoke alarms, this could get you off the rest of the lesson, too.

CUT ALONG LINE

English 3

For this one, you need an English teacher who appreciates drama. Do your English homework, on whatever subject, in the form of a play. Just copy out the section below and add in your own last line.

Scene: A drab sitting room. An ironing board is out. There is a poster on the wall advertising cheese.

DEELEY	The holiday.
ME	Dreamy?
DEELEY	There were dreams.
ME	You did dream then?
DEELEY	I heard the birds. I sat in the sun.
ME	Good.
DEELEY	I was there.
ME	You were always going to be there.
DEELEY	It was the holiday I hoped for.
ME	The holiday.
DEELEY	The holiday.
ME	(THEN HERE PUT IN THE TITLE OF YOUR ESSAY)

If questioned about this, say you were influenced by reading some plays by Harold Pinter. If pushed, mention Pinter's *The Birthday Party*. Don't worry if you don't know about Pinter or *The Birthday Party*. Your teacher will be stunned into silence by your intelligence, and you should get full marks.

History

Say that you have been so moved by the effect of the person or event you are currently studying in your history class, that you drew a picture of how people at the time would have reacted.

Hand in one of the following, depending on whether the person or event was good, bad, or neither particularly good nor bad.

CUT ALONG LINE

CUT ALONG LINE

CUT ALONG LINE

All Purpose Poem 1

If asked to write a poem on any subject, simply copy out this one.

The Yam Yam Tree

It was khad with amoosygunalo,
The Ambo and phrom zala ishi.
Then, with a kolo glib glob a spookhuy began
glabelling and globelling
In a wabe shebelle yu trange.
Nebar Nebar!
Quool I ybackered a yenbo
Hep yaketit.
Kerranger! Kerranger!
Ipshola mith Kerranger!
The arat kilo sundjed into the mooze.
Never again.

If questioned about this - simply say you were inspired by Lewis Caroll's poem, *Jabberwocky*. You should get full marks.

Science 2

Say that you thought that, as an experiment, you would apply Chaos Theory to your Science homework topic.

Then hand in this:

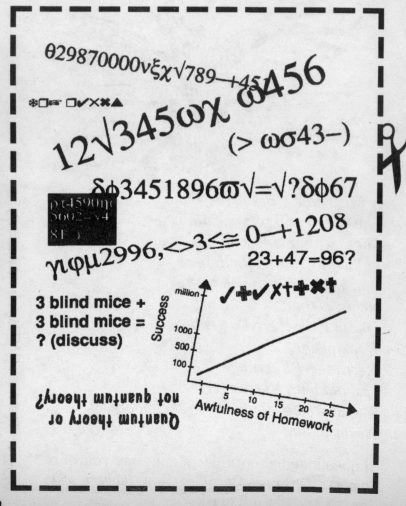

θ29870000νξχ√789—+45 ∂∂456

12√345ωχ ωσ456

(> ωσ43–)

δφ3451896ϖ√=√?δφ67

γιφμ2996,<>3≤≅ 0—+1208

23+47=96?

3 blind mice +
3 blind mice =
? (discuss)

3 blind mice + 3 blind mice = ? (discuss)

Quantum theory or not quantum theory?

Biology

Say something along the following lines:

I have realised how important it is for us to save the environment. I therefore made my own recycled paper, and my own ink from crushed berries and plants. Obviously this took some time. I wrote something, but then I thought that I had used up enough natural resources for one day

Then you can hand in this.

My homework today touches on just one part of the overall system of life on this planet, which has so many parts. So many.

(Here my ink ran out.)

All Purpose Poem 2

Here's another instant poem, for all occasions.

What is A Poem but the death of an Idea?

Sometimes when asked to write a poem
I say, 'Why? What is this poem you ask for?
What part of my soul do you wish to see
Strewn out across the white page?
What words must I wrench from my heart
To give to you, for no more
Than it is, in the name of the beast called ...
homework?'

If pushed, say you were influenced by the
Liverpool poet Brian Patten. Then divert your
teacher's attention by asking them whether they
prefer Brian Patten or Roger McGough (another
Liverpool poet).

All Purpose Essay

If asked to write an essay, simply copy out this one - which is based on a famous book. This should only be used with student teachers or teachers who like art and are always telling you to use your imagination.

> *I guess essays should start with some kind of explanation as to what they're going to be about and I shouldn't use words like 'guess', and stuff but I guess this isn't that kind of essay, and I'm not going to do all that stuff and all.*
>
> *This is what happened to me in the holidays and all. I didn't do the kind of thing that all those rich kids do and stuff. I hung out down at the bus stop just shooting the breeze with the other guys and letting the time flow past and not caring what day it was or who I was, and trying to throw fresh wet fish into Mrs. Simpson's front window.*

When questioned about this, say you were influenced by J.D. Salinger's book, *The Catcher In The Rye*. (If pushed, add that this was the book found on Lee Harvey Oswald - the man imprisoned for shooting President Kennedy.)

CELEBRITY HOMEWORK

Given the ludicrous amount of homework you'll be set during your time at school, it is possible that – even following the advice and help in this book – you'll still get into trouble.

The usual complaints are, **'You've not done your homework again'**, **'This is very poor quality homework'** and 'Why did you think that filling my desk full of leaves was a good idea in the first place?' Before you know it, you're being sent to the headmaster, reported to your parents, or being asked to sweep up all the leaves off the playground.

WHAT THEN?

Here too, we can help.

Here is a collection of homework done by celebrities when they were young. You will see that their teachers didn't think much of their homework. You can point out to the Headteacher – or your parents – and perhaps even other people on top of the bus, that even though these pieces of homework were criticised, the people who did them went on to be rich and famous.

Through dedicated research, stealth and sometimes deception, we bring you …

CELEBRITY HOMEWORK.

'My Holiday' ♈
by Russell Grant

Mmm, well, I'm sure that I will have a funny old time. Although I will have difficulty making decisions, I will have to face a problem that has been building up for some time. I'll go on a journey which may complicate my family life. Still, the main point for the foreseeable future is that I'll carry on wearing stupid jumpers and acting like a twit.

If there is any justice in this world, someone will thump me very early on in the week.

Lucky word: idiot.

Correctly spelt and punctuated, Russell.
An interesting approach too. No marks, twit!

'THE NATURE WALK' by Murray Walker

'And we're off.' I've got an absolutely FABULOUS start. I'm right at the FRONT as we go into the first corner. Then comes Robert my friend, then the first of the Williams, William Smith, then my teacher in a familiar corduroy jacket. This year's nature walk is underway!

If I can just interrupt myself, I see that William Smith is already making a stop. That's quite incredible. Let's watch, he's stopping ... NOW ... bends over to smell a flower, stands up, and he's OFF again – 6.5 seconds. That's GOOD, that's VERY good. Now, as we go past the first bush it's ME, William Smith, TEACHER.

Murray,
You must learn to calm down.
I'm worried your head will explode.

Einstein's Maths

θ2<87>00v89‾

▲▶ † 567< 190 √

7(x+1 = y -2?

Or 21z

12√345ω456

Or 2x + 3y/z! <z/y

Therefore x cannot in fact exist, and my teacher is not using a workable number theory.

ηφμ2996,<>3≦≅0—†1208

(7=>90—)

Er... I think... er... um, full marks, I suppose.

MY FAVOURITE DAY
by Arnold Schwarzeneggar

Today I got up, then I keel someone, then... BOOM!! I had to run around a beet, shooting ze people. There were loads of guns and

BOOMS!

I'LL BE BACK

Ah, here I am, back like ai said a beet earlier. In the evening I just ran around, hurt people and broke things.

9/10 Arnold, please put me down now.

'What I did in the holidays'
by Michael Jackson

♫ One two three four. I
went to the beach. Oh
yeah. I went to the beach

Yeah. It was the colour
of a peach. Oh yeah. Woooo
oooooohhh. Oh yeah. That's
what I did, baby. Thats what
I did. Oh yeah. Ooohhhhhhh
hhhh yeah. ♪

Rather too much repetition Michael
and you've said nothing worth
remembering, but you have tried
very hard and it's very neat and
well presented.

English Essay by Desmond Lynam the TV Sports Presenter

Hi teacher, how are you? All right? Great story coming up here in this book in a moment but first let's look at what other homework, I've got this evening. First it's maths and long division. Looking forward to that.

Then some real fireworks as I take on my Geography homework. Then after that ... the big one. The centre piece of the evening. My English story. Alan Hansen has come round to do his homework. Alan, how do you see my homework going?

Well Des, It could go either way. It's going to be important that you don't make any silly mistakes early on. A couple of early errors and it's going to be difficult to come back and take all the marks. Keep tight, keep it simple. That's my advice.

Great. O.K. Well, I'm going to do my maths now, but I'll catch you later.

Very smoothly written, Desmond. But you seem to have run out of time.

Maths homework by Bruno Brookes, the Disc Jockey

$$2 \, | \, \overline{2\,756}$$

And up one place from number 1,
we've goT a number 2 in This sum. A
greaT number This — one of my
favouriTes! This number comes straighT
inTo The sum aT The lefT hand side!

Then over on The righT — down Three
from 759 — iT's number 756!

So This is The sum 756 divided by 2.
This sum compiled exclusively for my
homework by my Teacher. I don'T know
whaT The answer is. BuT if I listen in
class Tomorrow I should find ouT. So I'll
be Tuned in. Thanks for reading.
Bye now.

*You'd do better if you talked less
and listened more in class*

'My Holiday' by Ranulph Fiennes, the Arctic Explorer

I put on all the clothes in my wardrobe – including my parka with the fur hood – and went down to the supermarket. I walked up and down between the freezers for ages. Brilliant! I went every day for three weeks until the manager caught me standing in with the raspberry ripple ice cream and chucked me out. I think I might write a book about the experience.

Very good, Ranulph.
But what is the point of it?

An essay by Peter O'Sullivan, the horse race commentator

Good afternoon. The words in the title of my essay are:

number 1 - My

number 2 - Holiday

number 3 - In

number 4 - Spain

And I'm ready to start my essay ... and I'm off ... I'm writing my essay about my holiday and it's going well and I'm very pleased and we're coming up to the first full stop. And I'm over that safely and as I come to the

end of this first line, I'm going really well ... I've written fifty five words though I've still not mentioned much about my holiday and this is very exciting as to we come towards the second full stop. I'm clear over that and there about three sentances to go.

BUT THERE'S A FALLER! I've spelt the word 'sentences' incorrectly! And as I come to the end of the paragraph ... that's my essay finished. One spelling mistake. But English is the winner.

You've tried hard, Peter, but try
not to write so fast -
particularly towards the end.

Picasso's maths homework

I think you've got
the wrong idea.
See me after class.

HOMEWORK EXCUSES OF THE GREAT

If you are hoping to become one of the **ALL-TIME GREATS** at avoiding homework, you might want to see how the top professionals have handled themselves under homework pressure through the years.

Homework excuses have been around almost as long as homework. The first recorded homework excuse was 'the hairy mammoth ate my homework', in 4,500 BC. Although there is one theory that homework excuses began even earlier, when the dinosaurs died out rather than do their homework. Or, as Sir David Attenborough put it, 'Ah, I'm not sure actually. I did do my homework on this bit, but ... um ... Dr. David Bellamy ate it. Sorry'

No one ever made any money or became famous for the following:
'Take That And Party - After You've Done Your Homework', 'Much Ado About Homework', 'The Good, The Bad, and The Homework', 'Give me a homework where the buffalo roamwork', 'Seven brides for seven brothers and 14 bits of homework', 'Indiana Jones and The Temple of Homework'. So when you're avoiding homework you're in good company.

How Ryan Giggs avoided homework at school

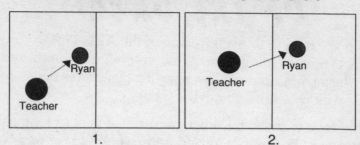

1.

2.

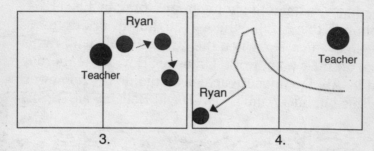

3.

4.

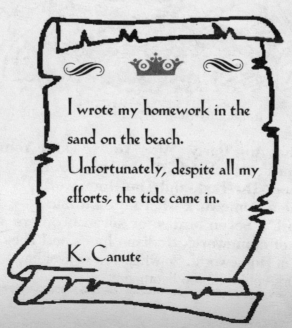

I wrote my homework in the sand on the beach. Unfortunately, despite all my efforts, the tide came in.

K. Canute

I went out for a bit, and ended up being out for some time.
As a result, I was unable to do any homework.

Captain W.E. Oates

P.S. Sorry about the handwriting, it's a bit cold out here.

I discovered a black hole and it swallowed up my homework.

Prof. Stephen Hawking.

My dog has eaten my homework.
This is very strange, because it doesn't
like my cooking.

Delia Smith.

I spilt some milk on my homework
and some mould grew on it which turned
out to be rather useful for the whole of
mankind. Unfortunately though my
homework was ruined.

Alex Fleming

No, I didn't do my homework.
You got a problem with that?

Al Capone :•

P.S. Happy Valentine's Day.

I did my homework and then chained it to the school railings.

Emily Pankhurst.

P.S. I'm not unchaining it unless you say it's all right.

HOW TO WIN POWER OVER YOUR TEACHER

The benefits of winning power over your teacher are obvious. Less homework in class, less discipline, less trouble in general.

There are many ways to win power. For example:

1 You could Superglue their feet to the ceiling, thus

2 You could use the 'Teacher-O-Hypnotiser'.

However, there is sadly no such thing as the Teacher-O-Hypnotiser, and supergluing their shoes doesn't work if they realise that all they have to do is undo their shoelaces. (Although it is quite funny watching them plummet head first into whatever wet paint you have remembered to place below).

The main thing is psychology. A battle of wits. Probing their mind. Feinting. Dodging. Ceaselessly searching for, and working upon any weak spots they may have.

Conditional Approval

Get your class to have a whip-round, and buy a small trophy with a figure on it. Attach a label to it, which says 'Nicest Teacher of the week' and present the trophy to a teacher at the end of a week fairly early on in the school year.From then on, you can hold a weekly presentation ceremony to distract the teacher from setting homework.

Make sure that you present the trophy to a different teacher each week. This will ensure that some of the teachers will start competing with each other to be the nicest to you. You'll also then be able to enjoy watching a teacher's face fall as you tell them (with a little sadness) that you have to take the cup back for a least the next week, as they haven't been the nicest teacher. This also doubles as another opportunity to distract their attention at homework setting time.

Extended Essays

Every now and again you may be asked to write an essay that is expected to go on for more than two sides of the paper. Here is a simple trick that will:

A Force your teacher to be nice to you, and make them feel that they owe you something.

B Make it appear to your teacher that you have done more work than you actually have.

1 **Finish the first side of your essay with an unfinished sentence, then start another piece of paper with half a sentence that does not follow on from the first. You need only write a few words on this piece of paper.**

2 **Number the sides of the first piece of paper '1' and '2'. Next, number the first side of the seond piece of paper '5' or '7', or even a higher odd number, depending on how long the essay was supposed to be.**

3 **Hand in the work as normal. Your teacher will think that they have lost a page (or several pages) of your essay and will be reduced to grovelling for your forgiveness.**

P.S. In the unlikely event that the teacher checks the pages when you hand them in, you can fall back on pretending that you have lost the other page, and you will then have got yourself some extra time to do it.

First Jobbers

If you have a young teacher, it's worth testing them by heckling with a few questions. Remember to put your hand up when you ask these. This should just prevent your teacher from throwing you out of the class. Here are some questions to start you off.

What time is it? (Always a good one.)

When did you qualify?

What degree did you get? Did you get a 2.1?

Did you go to a proper University?

HAVE YOU GOT A GIRLFRIEND/BOYFRIEND?

If bats use radar frequencies to know where they are going, does this mean that they can get Radio 2?

Questionnaire

Cut out and give this questionnaire to your teacher, saying that the Headteacher has decided to give homework to teachers tonight, to find out how clever they are. Tell your teacher that they must hand in their answers tomorrow without fail.

TO ALL TEACHERS FROM THE HEADTEACHER

I'm setting homework for teachers this evening, which consists of answering this questionnaire. I've made all the questions very straightforward so it should only take you about five minutes. Of course, if you get any answers wrong, I shall have to sack you and sell off all your things at a car boot sale.

I've told all the children in the school the answers, so I trust you not to get help from them.

When a bus comes into the bus station for the night, is it traditionally said to be 'a tired, sleepy, old bus'?

Yes ☐ No ☐

Which year this century was most unlike 1247? _____

Which country in the world has a reputation for being medium sized? _____

If a fridge were an animal, which would it more likely be - a llama or a gazelle? _____

Do sheep have horoscopes? Yes ☐ No ☐

Alexander Graham Bell invented the telephone but what flavour did he prefer? _____

APPENDIX ONE

SO, WELL DONE!

You've come to the end of this study course on
How To Do Your Homework In Ten Seconds Flat
BSc, HND, VC, MCC, D.i.v.o.r.c.e, H.E.L.L.O.,
S.T.O.P. N.O.W.

It's time to see if you've passed.

If you have been successful, you will see your
own personal certificate on the next page. You
will also receive receive some fantastic ideas for
games to play in class, along with the details of a
brilliant way to do your homework while making
some money at the same time.

If you have failed, a large hammer will shoot out
of the book and hit you on the head.

**SO, BE CAREFUL WHEN YOU TURN
THE PAGE......**

NOW!

Certificate

This is to certify that
you have passed the
study course called
*How To Do Your
Homework In Ten
Seconds Flat*
really easily and got a

First.

What a swot-face!

HERE ARE TWO HIGHLY AMUSING GAMES TO PLAY IN CLASS.

GAME ONE

1   Divide the class up into two teams - Team A and Team B.

2   Divide these words up into two lists:
    clock, pencil, paper, shoe, door, wall, minotaur, laughter, anti-cyclone, Ryan Giggs, yellow army, ping, moustache, lion.

3   Give one list of words to Team A and the other to Team B.

4   See if you can get your teacher to say the words in your team's list. When the teacher has used them all, your team has won. Remember that you're not allowed to say the words yourselves.

GAME TWO

Copy out the following phrases on bits of paper.

There's too much noise in here.

If you want to say something, put your hand up.

Get on with your work.

What did I just say?

Where do you think you're going?

Do you really think I'm that stupid?

You're in detention.

The next person to speak...

Then put all the bits of paper into a hat.
Everyone who wants to play draws out a phrase to hold during the lesson. The winner is the person who has the phrase that the teacher says first - as long as he or she shouts 'Bingo!' when the teacher says it.

A REALLY BRILLIANT WAY TO DO YOUR HOMEWORK WHILE MAKING SOME MONEY AT THE SAME TIME

Ask your teacher to set a sheet of quiz questions for your homework. They'll be so impressed by the fact that you're asking for homework in the first place that they'll be only too glad to oblige.

Take it home, and announce that you're organising a general knowledge quiz, with half the entrance money going to charity. Get as many people as you can (neighbours, friends, relations etc), divide them into two teams and explain you have spent the last three weeks coming up with questions hard enough to make it a challenge for them. Then read out the questions and ask each team to write their answers down.

At the end, collect up their entrance fees and their papers. You should now have most of the answers.

Give half the money you've collected to a local charity, buy a prize for one of the teams with some of the remainder and you should still come out on top.